Mosbas and the Magic Flute

MOSBAS AND THE MAGIC FLUTE

Jesse Bowman Bruchac

Bowman Books
Greenfield Center, New York

Forward by Joseph Bruchac

Published by Bowman Books
P.O. Box 308,
Greenfield Center, New York 12833

ISBN 0-87886-148-3

Library of Congress Number:

Printed in the United States of America

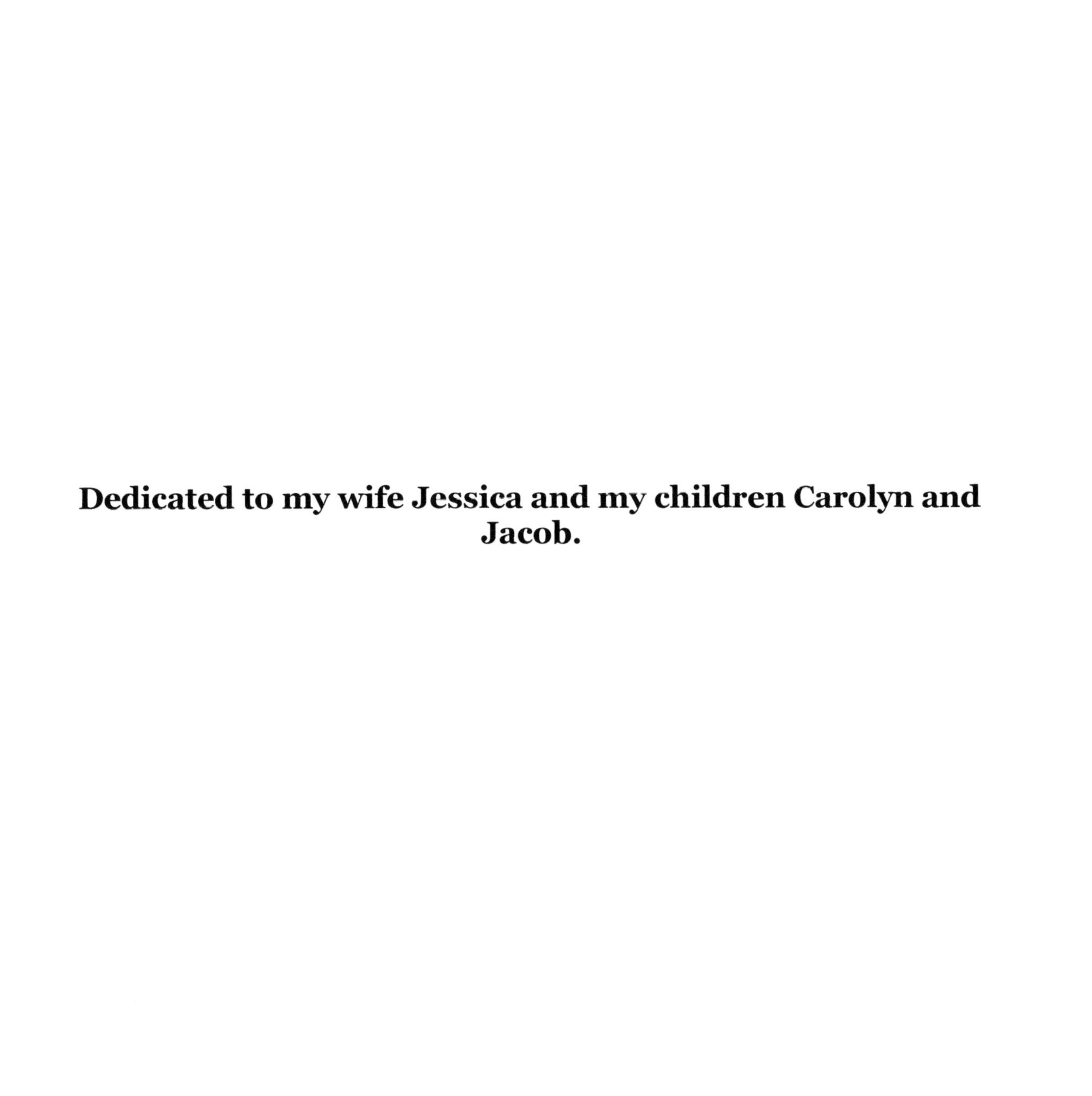

Dedicated to my wife Jessica and my children Carolyn and Jacob.

CHANGE REMAINS THE SAME
by Joseph Bruchac

Changer tales are found in every culture, stories that explain how places, animals, plants, and even the People were altered long ago by the actions of some powerful being. These stories help children see and think about the world around them. They often teach important lessons, for many of those changes take place when someone does something in the wrong way. For example, in one such story the dangerous animals are made smaller because they threaten to destroy the human beings.

The most important Changer in many of our Algonkian cultures is a great and ancient being who was the first to walk the earth in the shape of a human being. Often, the changes he puts into place are done in a benevolent way and are meant to help the People.

Among the Anishinabe (or Ojibway) nations to the west of us, he is known by such names as Nanabush and Manabozho. Among our own Alnonbak or Abenaki nations, his name is Gluskabe, Koluskap, Glooskap, or Kluskomba, depending on which Wabanaki language is being spoken.

Such tales were told and retold. They were often shaped in one way or another by the imagination and verbal skill of the individual storyteller. However, the essential lessons always remained. Such lessons include the teachings that change is always a part of life and that we must be aware of the consequences of our actions. They hold to the old tradition that stories both teach and entertain.

The following story of Kluskomba and his nephew Mosbas, is very much in that tradition.

THE WESTERN ABENAKI ALPHABET

8'8 A'a B'b C'c
D'd E'e G'g H'h
I'i J'j K'k L'l
M'm N'n O'o P'p
S's T't U'u W'w
Y'y Z'z

Vowels

8'8 A'a E'e I'i O'o U'u

Diphthongs

a8 ai ao i8 ia io
u8 iu ua ue ui

Key of the Pronunciation

The fifteen consonants of the Western Abenaki Alphabet are sounded as they are in English.

When a consonant or vowel are doubled the two letters are to be sounded as one, with the sound being prolonged.

When b, d are final letter of a word they are always sounded respectively, as p, t.

All the consonants must be sounded. There is no exception.

The letters F ,R, Q, V, or X are not used in the language.

When -gw and -kw are at the end of a word, the w is sounded as wha, and little more than a breath of air is expressed.

8 nasal sound like sk**un**k.

A as in **a**men.

B as in **b**oy.

Ch is sounded as '**ts**.'

E as in lab**e**l.

G is always hard, as in **g**ood and be**g**in.

H as in **h**ello.

I as in the double '**e**' in fr**ee.**

J is sounded like **dz** (ch and j are often interchanged).

K as in **k**ill.

L as in **l**oon.

M as in **mom**

N as in **n**urse.

O as in n**o**tice

P like **p**arty (p and b are often interchanged).

S like in the word **s**chool (s and z are often interchanged).

T like in the word **t**ime (t and d are often interchanged).

Ph never sounded as '**f**'. Always pronounce both letters, with the hard p sound followed by a short aspirate H sound.

U is sounded as '**u**' in **u**nion.

W sounded as the '**ew**' in fl**ew,** when followed by a vowel like '**w**' in **w**e.

Y like '**y**' in the word **y**oung.

See page 21 for more about the Western Abenaki Language.

Mosbas ta Medawlinn8gan Pikw8gan

Mosbas and the Magic Flute

N8wad, pm88zo wskinnos lewizo Mosbas, nam8nimiza Klosk8ba. Klosk8ba kizihap agmatta wji pegwis wji m8jasaik. K8dak Klosk8ba pita medawlinno niba azwagagagia. Mosbas ta Klosk8ba nismigakaadit msalkil aodiikok. Majimiwi w'kawhoabanik, kanwa Mosbas 8da wlidah8zowi.

Wz8mi agajew8bat. 8da nadodemawawiak awaaskwak nibaoak agmak. Namihap wid8bak nibaoak, ni adoji kakaswi gw8gwenahla. Ni, w'kiztop 8dakaw8 w'zasiza.

"Waj8na pita medawlinn8gan," tbidaw8zo, "ta n'kizi wijokap s8waiwi. Kizilla n'wijokamegonji meskaw8 nizwiak?"

N8wad, Long ago there was a young man named Mosbas. He was the nephew of the great Kluskomba. Kluskomba had shaped himself from the leftover dust of creation. Being made from creation's dust, Klusbomba had great power and the ability to create new things. His nephew, Mosbas had stood by his side during many battles. Victory was always theirs, but Mosbas was not happy.

He was far too shy to ever ask any of the female creatures to marry him. He saw all of his friends marrying and starting families of their own, while he grew more and more jealous of their happiness. One day, Mosbas decided he needed to visit his uncle.

"He has great power," he thought, "and I have helped him so many times. Perhaps he could use his powers to help me find a wife?"

Mosbas odosan wigw8mek w'zasisa. W'pk8gnap ni kachkano kl8ganek. W'nodam al8miwi awani ida, "Pidiga." Ni, Mosbas pidigad wigw8mek. Ag8mek kchi skweda nidali Klosk8ba abo.

"N'zasis," Mosbas idam, "chig8wiwi kchi k'wlipamkanninawal, 8da n'kiziw meskaw8 nizwiak. N'kadi waj8n8k waligijik nizwiak ta aw8sisak. Nikw8bi n'wawtam ni p8paami gez8wadon." Nilil klozow8ganal Klosk8ba w'wawtamenol mawigenol. W'kiztop wd'achwi wijoka nam8nimiza. Wikwenemen pikw8gan nodak.

"M8jado io pikw8gan kpiwi, ponemen kd'asabaskedonikok ni pikwawa. Wikwem8ji wlit8gwat awaaskwa kiak. Wd'aoji k'nizwiak ta k'milegon lakamigwezow8gan.

Mosbas visited the lodge of his uncle. He bent and scratched at the bark door. A voice from within said, "Pidiga, enter." Mosbas entered the lodge. There across from him, behind a great fire sat Kluskomba.

"N'zasis, my uncle," Mosbas said, "even after all our great adventures, I'm unable to win the heart of any of the female creatures. More than anything, I want to have a good wife and start a family of my own. I realize this is what really matters." These words rang true to Klusbomba. He decided to help his nephew. He reached into his pouch and pulled forth a magic flute.

"Take this pikongan to the edge of the forest, put it to your lips and blow and a beautiful sound will come out, it will call the heart of one of the female creatures to you. She will be your wife and give you a family."

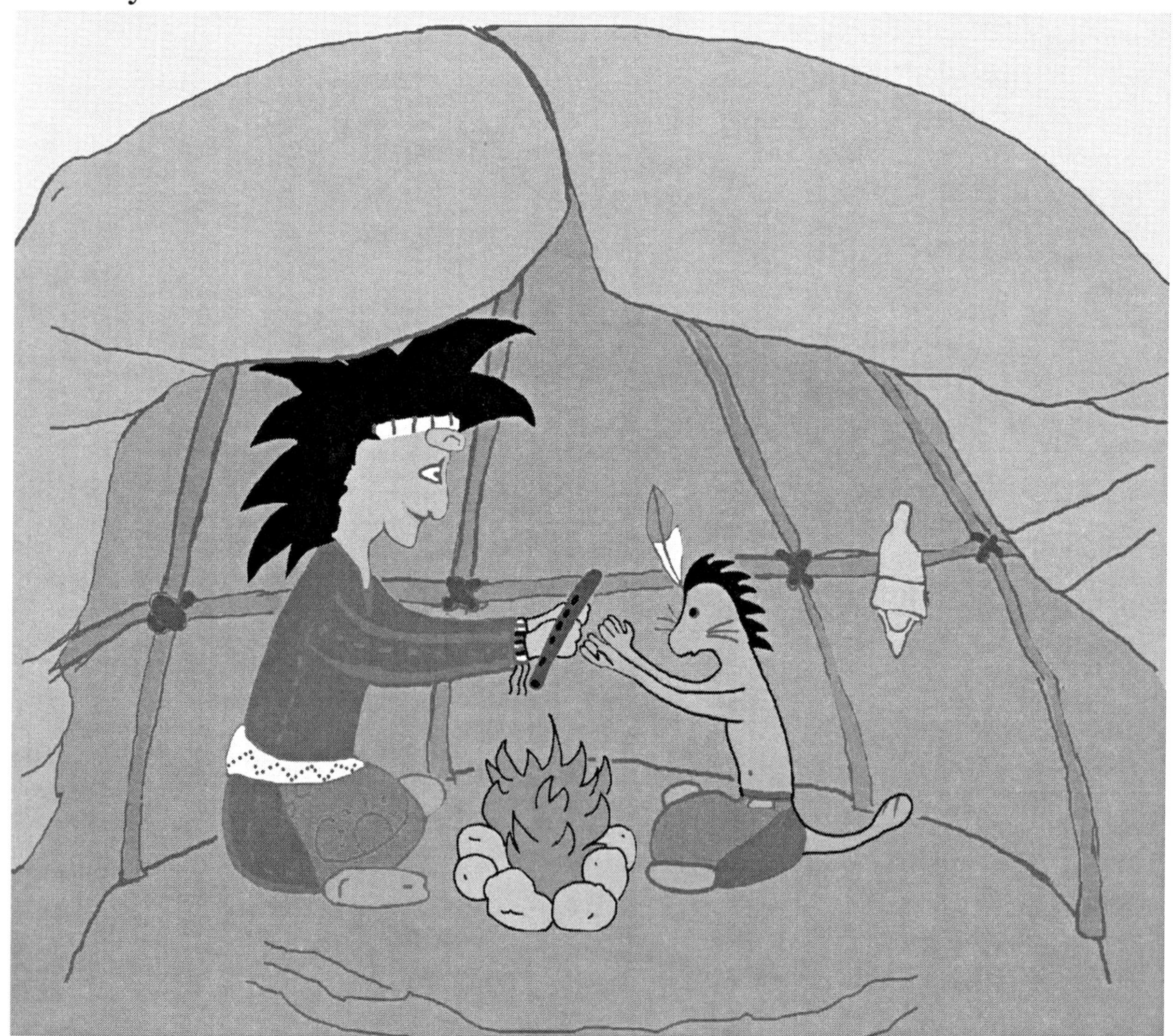

Mosbas pita wd'iksidawi. "Kchi wliwni n'zasis," wd'idam. Niga kezosa s8sasagosa li kpiwi.

T8ni adoji paia kpiwi, w'ponemen pikw8gan asabaskedonikok ta pikwa. Kaalata, wlit8gwat. Askawiha. Wikwenaba awaasskwa agmak? Ni namiha Medawihlaskwa bemidoo li agmak.

Mosbas was very excited. "Kchi wliwni n'zasis, great thanks my uncle," he said. Then he quickly left the lodge and headed straight for the forest.

As soon as he reached the edge of the woods, he put the flute to his lips and blew. Sure enough, it made a beautiful sound. He waited to see if what his uncle had said was true. Would it indeed call one of the female creatures to his side? Then he noticed someone circling above him. It was Medawihlaskwa, Loon Woman.

Benihl8t pasojiwi agma ni wd'lipodiga k8tikok. Kaalata, wikwenemen wlaw8gana Medawihlaskwa. Wlidah8zop, kanwa chiga namiha pmossat alin8gwezo ta8lawi kwigwigem.

"Nda n'kiziw nibao kwigwigem" tbidah8zo, "pakalmegwat n'zasis wawtamba. Ibitta n'gwagwaji io pikw8gan pazegweda. Nd'achwi wlito mina lintow8gan."

Ni, ponemen pikw8gan asabaskedonikok ni pikwawa mina. Kanwa, poskwena wlaw8gana Medawihlaskwa. Bemidoo nebesisek nopaiwi pebonkik. Askwa k'kizi nodam wd'linto ni lintow8gan Mosbas kizitop wji agma n8wad.

She landed near him and began rubbing against his legs. It had worked. He had called the heart of Loon Woman. He was happy at first, but then he noticed that as Loon Woman walked, she waddled from side to side. She looked a little bit like a duck.

"I can't marry a duck" he thought, "Surely my uncle would understand. I was just making sure this flute worked. I must play another song."

So, he put the flute to his lips and blew again. But by doing so, he broke the heart of Loon Woman. She flew off to a pond far to the north. There we can still hear her singing that song Mosbas played for her long ago.

Mosbas kizitop wlintow8gan mina ni askawiha mina. Nabiwi, ligedaho lihla agmak pizewakamigok s8khosa Nolkaskwa.

"N'wikwem8 Nolkaskwa! Nia n'wlalokahl8 pikw8ganek! Nikw8bi wji ali n'wawtamen, n'kizi wlito agwachi mawintow8gan. N'kizi wikwem8 mawigit phanem.

Mosbas played another beautiful song. Then he waited to see if it would work again. Soon, bounding towards him from the woods came Nolkaskwa, Deer Woman. Mosbas was even more excited.

"I have called the heart of Deer Woman! I'm really getting the hang of this flute! Now that I've figured it out, I can play an even better song. I can call an even better wife!"

Agma ponemen pikw8gan asabaskedonikok mina ni pikwawa, poskwena wlaw8gana Nolkaskwa, agma wibiwi kwelbosa ta ligedaho pedgo pizewakamigok.

Mina lintow8gan kizitop wlit8gwat. Mina wd'askawiha.

He put the flute to his lips again and blew, breaking the heart of Deer Woman, who just turned and bounded off back into the woods.

Just as before, the song he played as beautiful. Again he waited.

Nidali manossa pizewakamigok s8khosa Awasosskwa! "Wahoo!" Mosbas k8g8lewa, "n'wikwenemen wlaw8gana Awasosskwa. Wliphanem. Nd'awazigon kwanipok. Wlinod8kwkwat. Wawaldamen mziwi nbizonal. Adoji masgilek ta mlikigit w'kiziba agwachi nd'ikolzigw!"

Wz8mi wlidah8zo, kanwa achi wd'laldam adoji wlaloka kizitop wlintow8ganal.

"Kchi n'wlinod8baktahigad" tbidah8zop. "Ibitta nseda gwagwajitow8ganal ni n'kawhoa wlaw8gana Awasosskwa. Chaga n'wlito mina lintow8gan, n'kiziba wikwem8 p8paami wliphanem. Mziwikba gw8gwenak niak."

There lumbering out of the woods came Awasosskwa, Bear Woman! " Wahoo!" Mosbas cried, "I have called the heart of Bear Woman. She will be a great wife. She can keep me warm during the long winters. She is a great cook. She knows all the medicines. She's so big and strong she could even protect me!"

He was overjoyed, but he was also feeling impressed by how well he had done with his songs.

"I am clearly a gifted musician" he thought. "Just three tries and I have won the heart of Bear Woman. If I played another song, I could call the greatest wife of all. All would envy me and be jealous of me."

Lidah8zimek iolil adebadah8zow8ganal, w'ponemen ni pikw8gan asabaskedonikok mina. Kanwa, nikw8bi w'poskwenemen wlaw8gana Awasosskwa. Ni 8da wlimikawidah8ziw kwetgwihla Awasos, p8bapaami Awasosskwa.

Chiga namito Mosbas kadawi mina wlito lintow8gan, agwachi asma pikwawa w'zelegejagenagw wskijiwi pikw8ganek, poskwenemen pikw8gan nagwiwi agma ta pedgimila medawlinn8gan Klosk8bak ta abaziikok.

Thinking these twisted thoughts, he put that flute to his lips again to blow. However, the heart he broke this time was that of Bear Woman. It is a not a good idea to upset a bear, especially a bear woman.

When she saw Mosbas about to play that flute again, she reached out with one paw. Before he got out even a single note, she smooshed him down onto that flute, breaking it into many pieces beneath him and returning its magic to Kluskomba and the trees.

Chiga d8pkenemen weljia, Mosbas azwahap li Sagwazis.

Askwa pamgisgak, Sagwazis paami piwsisit 8daki wijiak wz8mi w'paghiminagw Awasosskwa. Askwa w'waj8nem pik8gnem w'beskwana wji ali w'gwagwen8 wskijiwi pikw8ganek wlawakatopba.

Daki, Sagwasiz w'meskaw8 nizwidijik, kanwa ni kdak 8tlokaw8gan.

When she lifted her paw, Mosbas had been changed into the very first weasel.

To this day, Weasel is smaller than all his brothers from being crushed by Bear Woman and still has a crooked broken back from being driven down onto that magic flute he played so well.

Eventually, Weasel did find himself a perfect wife, but that is another story.

While the magic flute given to Mosbas was misused and eventually destroyed, a bit of its magic remains. We can still hear it in the beautiful melodies played on Native flutes. Be they in traditional songs, imitations of animal and bird songs, the sounds of the wind, or improvisations.

The Native flute has also long been used by many Native American peoples in courting. Often when a man fell in love with a woman, rather than approaching her, he would compose a melody for her on the flute, with hopes she would at least take notice of him, or even in some cases accept it as a proposal of marriage.

In some Native communities these courting songs would be given words and later sung as lullabies to any children that couple might have together. This tradition has left us with many haunting Native American lullabies that were originally played as courting songs.

Wji W8banaki8dwaw8gan
About the Western Abenaki Language

Western Abenaki (also known as Sokoki, St. Francis, or Abenaki-Penobscot) is a linguistic subdivision of the Eastern Algonquian languages which are a subgroup of the greater Algonquian languages, a subgroup of Algic languages. Prior to European contact Eastern Algonquian was comprised of 17 languages which stretched from Newfoundland south into North Carolina.

Eastern Abenaki	Mohegan
Western Abenaki	Montauk-
Etchemin	Narragansett
Delaware	Nanticoke
Nipmuck	Carolina
Mahican	Algonquian
Malecite	Powhatan
Passamaquoddy	Quiripi-
Wampanoag	Naugatuck
Mi'kmaq	Piscataway

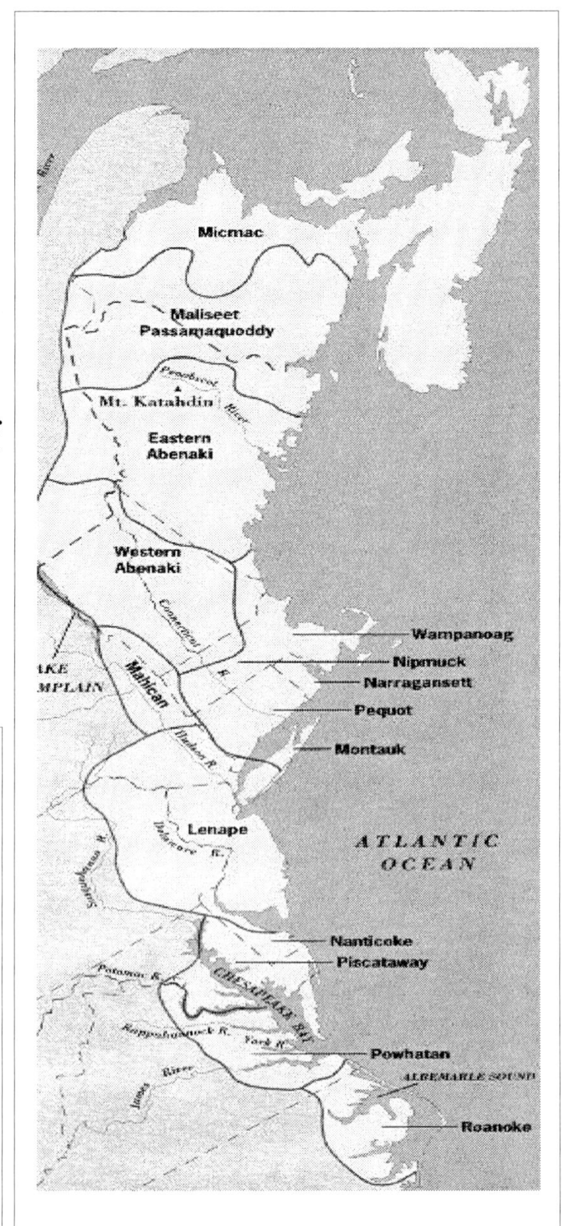

The Algonquian language family was once one of the largest in America, extending from Manitoba to the eastern seaboard and down to North Carolina, and survival for the early English settlers required their learning the language. The Algonquians, however, who had a long tradition of bilingualism, learned English and in time, English became so dominant in the mixed society that speaking most of the Algonquian languages died out virtually completely. By the 20th century only a few dozen Canadian Abenaki still spoke the Western Abenaki language. Today a revitalization of the language is well underway. This would not be possible without the efforts of many who see the great value in its preservation.

According to Blair Rudes, a specialist in past and present American Indian languages from the University of North Carolina at Charlotte, "For the most part, subjects would come first, objects would come second, verbs would come last. But sometimes objects would come after verbs. Adverbs would frequently come at the very beginning of a sentence."

The Algonquian languages are considered among the easier [Native American languages] in terms of pronunciation for a European. They tend to be somewhat like Spanish, for example, in terms of having a consonant-vowel-consonant-vowel structure.

Algonquian languages are agglutinative, meaning prefixes and suffixes add meaning. This often results in words being very long and entire sentences being expressed within a single word.

Map of Algonquian Speaking Peoples

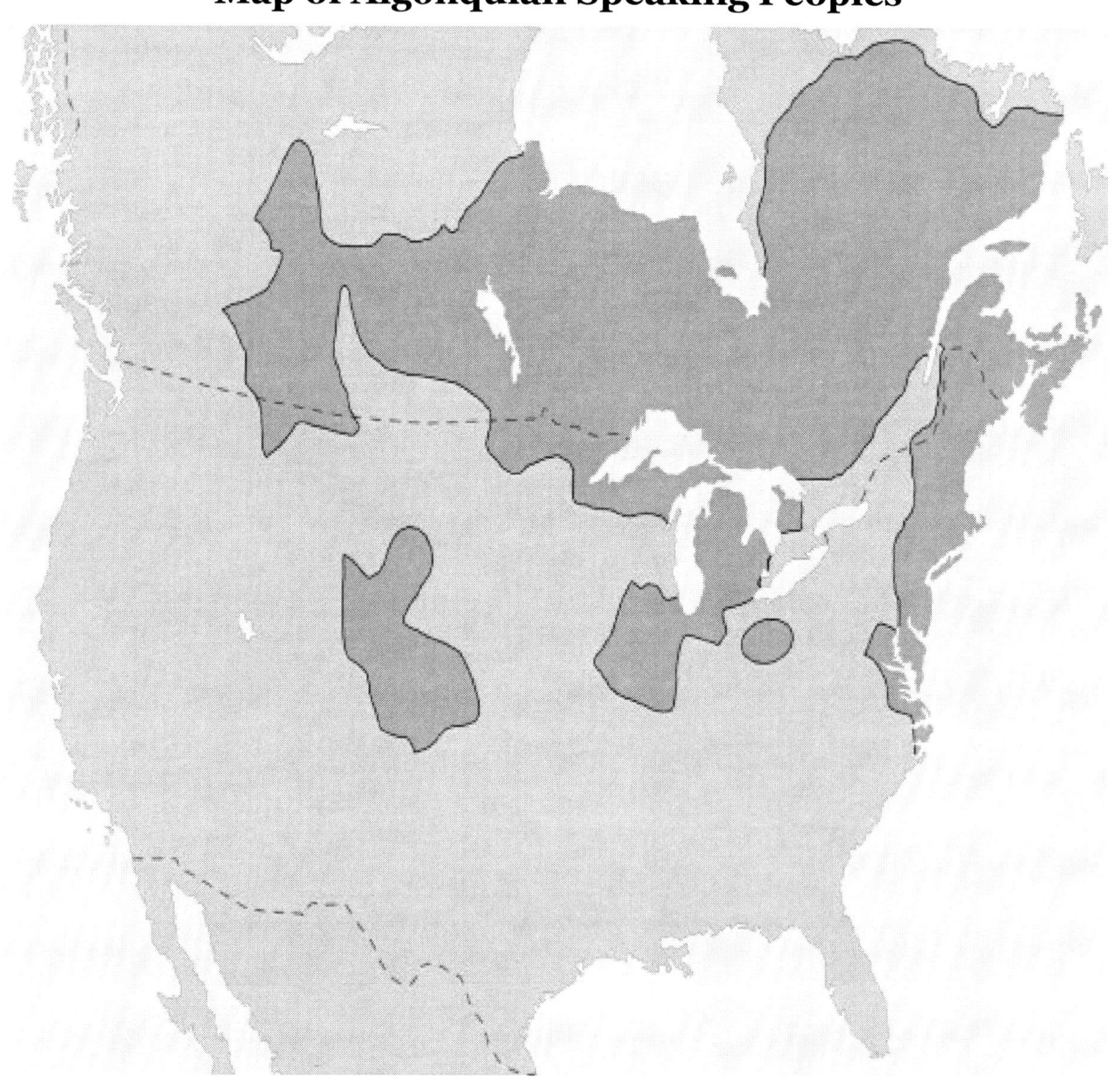

Originally one dialect flowed into the next making communication between neighbouring Algonquian speaking peoples possible. As peoples were displaced, many of the dialects were absorbed and incorporated, making Western Abenaki an amalgamation of northeastern Algonquian languages. The history of Odanak, Quebec, where the language has survived, is that of a transient refuge community that, from 1670 on gave shelter to Algonquian speaking peoples from all over the northeast. This has clearly had an effect on the language spoken today, compared to the dialects which were first recorded. The primary tribal groups who contributed to modern Western Abenaki are the Sokwakis, Penecooks, and the Cowassucks. In addition the language has been influenced by the Schaghticokes, Woronoco, Mohicans, Mahicans, Nipmucks, Pocumtucks, Penobscots, Androscoggins, Missiquois and Amonoscoggins, as members from these tribes moved in and out of the community of Odanak during the 18th and 19th centuries. Other tribal groups who spoke early forms of Western Abenaki include the Amoskeay, Cocheco, Coos, Nashua, Ossipee, Pemigewasset, Pequaket, Piscataqua, Souhegan, and the Winnibisauga.

With the extinction of most dialects of Eastern Algonquian, an understanding of these languages is still possible by examining Western Abenaki, making its preservation as a spoken language that more more vital.

Eastern Algonquian languages have left their mark forever as hundreds of place names throughout the northeast. Below are just a few examples:

MASSACHUSETTS from "Msajosek" meaning, where there are many hills.

COOKSAKEE from "Skogsaki", meaning, snake land

CONNECTICUT from "Kwenitegok", meaning, at the long river

MANHATTAN from "Menahanitan", tidal island, or from "Menahanaden", mountain island

Many other words have been incorporated into English as loanwords. There are about 150 generally used Algonquian Indian words in the English language today, examples include: toboggan, moccasin, caribou, skunk, tomahawk, muskrat, moose, wigwam, and sagamore.

While Abenaki has no gender, there is a similar distinction between animate and inanimate nouns. Much as you would not say in English, "Look at that woman, his hair is nice," animate nouns in Abenaki are always used with the animate forms of verbs and adjectives, likewise, inanimate forms are always used together, giving the noun the central role in determining the forms taken by the other parts of speech in any given statement. In general, living things are animate. A tree, for example, is considered animate, but inanimate if it's been cut down. A hill devoid of vegetation is inanimate, while one lush with growth becomes animate. Certain diseases are also respectfully raised to the animate class, along with objects held indispensable, or in high regard such as snowshoes, toboggans and tobacco. The parts of any animate thing are also usually inanimate. Within this book you will see both animate (pluralized with -k) and inanimate (pluralized with -l) nouns and the coinciding animate and inanimate conjugation of adjectives and verbs. Abenaki verbs also have a third classification of passive/neutered forms for intransitives, which are used when speaking of no direct object. These intransitive verbs often take the same, or a similar form of the animate verb, but always use the inanimate conjugations. Most Abenaki verbs are ambitransitive, having both transitive (animate and inanimate) and intransitive forms, while others have unique intransitive forms.

"A study of the verb reveals the high degree of inflectional complexity the language has. It is because of this verbal richness that philologists have called the Indian language a language of verbs." - Steven Laurent

Western Abenaki is still a spoken language, and luckily the research, dedication and love for the language of many individuals has left us with many resources to draw from in our efforts to preserve it.

The language has been defined as one that is so soft and fluttery it would not disturb the birds and compared to the sound of a babbling brook.

The inclusion of the Western Abenaki language in this book will hopefully act as yet another resource to help in the preservation and revitalization efforts already underway, givings young and old readers alike another chance to use, improve or simply refresh their abilities within this living language.

The index of words that follow should be of great use to those interested in getting better acquainted with both the language and the story of Mosbas.

8

8da no, not (also nda)
8dakaw8 visit him (also odakaw8)
8daki than, rather than, instead of (also ndaki)
8tlokaw8gan a telling, a story, a tale (also 8tlok8gan)

A

abaziikok in, to, at, of, on the trees
abo he sits

achi also, too
adebadah8zow8ganal twisted, tangled thoughts
adoji then, there, so much
ag8mek on the other side, across
agajew8bat he is a bashful man, he is a shy man
agma him, her, his, hers, he, she
agmak to, in, of, at or, on him or her
agmatta himself, herself
agwachi actually, really, even
al8miwi inside
ali how, like, the way that, that, as, because, thus
alin8gwezo the way he/she looks, how he/she looks
aodiikok in wars, in fights
asabaskedonikok on lips, to lips
askawiha she/he waits for someone, she/he expects someone
askwa still, yet
asma not yet, never, before
aw8sisak children, infants
awaas a wild animal
awaaskwa a female wild animal
awaaskwak female wild animals
awani someone, who
awasos a bear
awasosskwa a female bear
azwahap she/he was changed, he is changed
azwato change something
azwagagagia change things

B

bemidoo he/she flies about

benihl8t she/he lands, she/he comes down

Ch

chaga if
chig8wiwi in spite of
chiga when

D

d8pkenemen he/she lifts it up
daki later on, at last

G

gez8wadon it is important
gw8gwenahla she/he becomes jealous
gw8gwenak they are jealous
gwagwajitow8ganal tries, attempts

I

ibitta only
ida he/she says, say
idam he/she says
io this (inanimate thing)
iolil these (inanimate things)

K

k'kizi you can, you are able to; you have already, you already
k'milegon he/she gives you
k'nizwiak your spouse
k'wlipamkanninawal our good journeys
kadawi wanting to
kakaswi more and more
k8dak for example, for instance, like, thus, therefore, even
k8g8lewa she/he call, cry, holler, yell, scream
k8tikok on his/her legs
kaalata indeed, surely, certainly, of course
kachkano he/she scratches
kanwa but, however
kasta times, so many times
katahla get ready, become prepared
kchi big, great, old
kd'asabaskedonikok to your

lips, on your lips, at your lips
kdak other, another, other one
kezosa he goes fast, walks fast
kiak to you, of you, in you, on you
kizihap she/he made (something animate)
kizilla perhaps, could be true
kizitop she/he made (something inanimate)
kl8ganek on the door, at the door
klosk8ba talking man, culture hero
klozow8gan a word, speech
klozow8ganal words
kpiwi the woods
kwanipok during the winter
kwelbosa turn around
kwetgwihla to become upset, upsets, upsetting
kwigwigem a duck

L

lakamigwezow8gan a family
lewizo his/her name, he or she is called
li to, towards, at, until, for; like, as
lihla towards someone or something
lidah8zimek think, decide, make up mind, the act of thinking
ligedaho he/she jumps
lintow8gan a song

M

masgilek a big animate thing
m8jado she/he bring something, carry something, take something; she/he flies away, she/he starts to fly
m8jasaik it is the beginning, in the beginning
majimiwi always
manossa he/she walks slowly
mawigenol they are better things, the correct things
mawigit he/she is better, he/she is correct
mawintow8gan a better song
medawihlaskwa loon woman
medawlinn8gan something that has shaman power, magic
medawlinno a shaman, a

magician
meskaw8 she/he finds finds him/her/someone
meskawa he/she finds (something animate)
mina again, more
mlikigit a strong person or animate thing
mosbas a mink
msalkil many (inanimate things)
mziwi everything
mziwikba everyone would, everyone could

N

nagwiwi under, beneath
n'gwagwaji I try
n'kadi I want to
n'kawhoa I win
n'kizi I can, a am able to; I have already, a already
n'kiziba I could
n'kiziw I can not
n'wawtam I understand
n'wawtamen I understand it, I understand the
n'wijokamegonji he/she will help me
n'wikwenemen I pull it, I take it, I draw it/the
n'wikwim8 I draw him/her, I pull him/her, I call forth him/her
n'wlalokahl8 I become good at doing
n'wlinod8baktahigad I am a good musician
n'wlito I make
n'zasis my uncle (my mother's brother)
n8kskwa a girl
n8wad long ago
nabiwi soon
nadodemawawiak she/he does not ask them
nam8nimiz nephew
nam8nimiza her/his nephew
namiha she/he sees (something animate)
namihap she/he saw (something animate)
namito she/he sees (something inanimate)
natami the first, first

nbizonal medicines
nd'achwi I should, I must, I need to
nd'awazigon she/he warms me
nd'ikolzigw she/he protects me
nda no, not
nebesisek at the pond
nhenol three inanimate things
ni that (inanimate thing); and; there, then, so
nia I, me, my
niba and should, then could
nibao marry
nibaoak they marry
nidali that place, there
niga then, so it is
nikw8bi now
nilil those (inanimate things)
nismigakaadit they fight as two
nizwiak my spouse
nizwidijik his/her spouse
nodak in a bag, from a bag, at a bag, on a bag
nodam he/she hears something
nolkaskwa deer woman
nopaiwi far away
nseda three times

O

odosan he/she went

P

p8bapaami very much more, too much, especially; once, formerly
p8paami much better, much more
pazegweda once, one time
paami more, better
paia he/she arrives
pakalmegwat surely, certainly
pamgisgak today
pasojiwi nearby, close
pebonkik in the north land, north, winter land
pedgimila give back, return
pedgo he/she returns
pegwis dust
phanem woman, wife
pidiga enter
pidigad he enters
pikw8gan a flute
pikw8ganek on, at, from a flute
pikwa he/she blow into an

instrument
pikwawa blow an instrument to call him/her
pita very
piwsisit a small animate one
pizewakamigok in the forest
pik8gnem bent and broken
pm88zo he/she lives
pmossat he/she walks
ponemen he/she puts or places something inanimate
poskwena he/she breaks something
poskwenemen he/she breaks it

S

s8khosa he/she is coming
s8sasagosa he/she goes straight
s8waiwi often, frequently
sagwasiz a weasel
skweda a fire

T

t8ni how, where
ta and
ta8lawi like, similar to
tbidah8zo he/she thinks
tbidah8zop he/she thought

W

w'beskwana his/her back
w'gwagwen8 he/she pushes him
w'kawhoabanik they won
w'kizi he/she can, he/she is able to; he/she has already
w'kiziba he/she could, he/she is able to
w'kiztop he/she decided
w'meskaw8 he found her
w'nodam he/she hears
w'paghiminagw she crushes him
w'pk8gnap he/she bent
w'ponemen he/she puts, places (something inanimate)
w'poskwena he/she breaks something
w'poskwenemen he/she breaks it
w'waj8nem he/she has something (inanimate)

w'wawtamenol he/she understood
w'zasiza his uncle (his mother's brother)
waj8n8k she/he have them
waj8na he/she has
waligijik good animate ones
wawaldamen he/she knows it, he/she knows the
wawtamba he/she could understand
wd'achwi he/she should, he/she could
wd'aoji he/she will be
wd'idam he/she says, he/she said
wd'iksidawi he/she is excited
wd'laldam he/she thinks
wd'linto he/she sings
wd'lipodiga he/she rubs
wd'losa he/she goes
weljia his/her hand
wibiwi only, just
wid8bak his/her friends
wigw8mek to a house, at a house, in a house, on a house, from a house
wijiak his/her brothers
wijoka he/she helps
wijokap he/she helped
wikwem8 he/she draws him/her, he/she calls him/her to come, he/she pulls him/her
wikwem8ji he/she will draw him/her
wikwim8p he/she has drawn him/her
wikwenaba could he/she pull, he/she could draw
wikwenemen she/he pull the inanimate thing, draw to him/her the (inanimate thing)
wji from, for, for the purpose of, about, in order to, so that, so as to, as for, since
wlaloka she/he work well, do good work, do something well
wlawakatopba he/she could/should have used well
wlaw8gan a heart
wlaw8gana her/his heart
wlidah8zo he/she is happy
wlidah8zop he/she was happy
wlidah8zowi he/she is not

happy (following 8da)
wlintow8gan a good song
wlimikawidah8ziw not a good idea (following 8da)
wlinod8kwkwat he/she is a good cook
wlintow8ganal good songs
wliphanem he/she is a good wife, a good woman
wlipikwaba he/she could blow in an instrument well
wlit8gwat it sounds beautiful, a beautiful sound
wlito he/she makes
wliwni thank you
wskijiwi upon
wskinnos a young man
wz8mi too much; because

Z

w'zelegejagenagw she/he crushes her/him